The Re

By Liza Charlesworth

ISBN: 978-1-339-02661-9

Art Director: Tannaz Fassihi; Designer: Tanya Chernyak
Photos © Getty Images and Shutterstock.com.

3 4 5 6 7 8 9 10   68   32 31 30 29 28 27 26 25 24

Printed in Jiaxing, China. First printing, August 2023.

■SCHOLASTIC

It is a hen.
The hen is red.

The hen has a big pen.
Peck, peck, peck!

The hen sits on eggs
in the pen.

Peck, peck, peck!
POP, POP, POP!

The red hen has ten chicks!

The ten chicks sit.

The ten chicks get fed.

Hug, hug, hug!
The red hen is a mom.